MW00618140

RECLAIM YOUR DAY

BY GIVING IT AWAY

live today well
COLLECTIVE

Copyright © 2020 by Mary Williams and Kara Becker

All rights reserved. This book or any portion thereof may not be reproduced or used in any manner whatsoever without the express written permission of the publisher.

ISBN 978-0-9992773-7-9

Scripture quotations are from New Revised Standard Version Bible: Catholic Edition, copyright © 1989, 1993 National Council of the Churches of Christ in the United States of America. Used by permission. All rights reserved.

Scripture texts in this work are taken from the New American Bible, revised edition © 2010, 1991, 1986, 1970 Confraternity of Christian Doctrine, Washington, D.C. and are used by permission of the copyright owner. All Rights Reserved. No part of the New American Bible may be reproduced in any form without permission in writing from the copyright owner.

Excerpts from the English translation of the Catechism of the Catholic Church for use in the United States of America Copyright © 1994, United States Catholic Conference, Inc. -- Libreria Editrice Vaticana. Used with Permission. English translation of the Catechism of the Catholic Church: Modifications from the Editio Typica copyright © 1997, United States Conference of Catholic Bishops—Libreria Editrice Vaticana.

www.livetodaywellco.com

MORNING OFFERING

the

journal

K. Becker & M. Williams
2020

contents

introduction

WHAT IS THE MORNING OFFERING?

As a new day dawns, the Morning Offering extends an invitation to you...a summons to draw nearer to the One who loves you most of all. Traditionally prayed first thing in the morning, the Morning Offering allows you to kneel humbly at God's feet and surrender the intentions of your whole heart into His loving care. Not only are your prayers, works, joys, and sufferings offered up to God during the Morning Offering, but your own intentions are united with those of the whole church as well.

Though multiple versions of the Morning Offering prayer exist, Father François-Xavier Gautrelet, S.J., is credited with composing the most widely used Morning Offering prayer to the Sacred Heart of Jesus. Father Gautrelet's version of the prayer, which was originally created in 1844 for his new Apostleship of Prayer, continues to be prayed daily by Catholics around the world.

His version of the Morning Offering follows below:

O Jesus, through the Immaculate Heart of Mary, I offer you my prayers, works, joys, and sufferings of this day for all the intentions of your Sacred Heart, in union with the Holy Sacrifice of the Mass throughout the world, for the salvation of souls, the reparation of sins, the reunion of all Christians, and in particular for the intentions of the Holy Father this month. Amen.

WHAT IS INSIDE THIS JOURNAL?

Inspired by the Morning Offering prayer, this journal utilizes both the tradition of scripture and simple, thoughtful prompts to allow you to offer your whole self to God.

For each entry of this ninety day journal, you'll find a scripture passage on which to meditate and a journaling page on which to write your prayers.

"In the beginning was the Word, and the Word was with God, and the Word was God." (John 1:1)

He was and is the Word. In Sacred Scripture, God calls us to draw near so that we may come to know Him more fully and rest with Him. For this reason, each day of this journal features a short scripture passage.

As you begin to reflect on the scripture of the day, you will notice that the first half of the scripture passage is written in a typed font while the second half of the passage is written in a script font. The page is designed in this way to encourage you to inhale while you read the first half of the scripture passage and then to exhale as you pray the second half.

We invite you to deepen your relationship with God by breathing the scripture passage slowly in and out. There is no need to adjust your breathing by taking long, slow, or deep breaths. Instead, just use your normal pattern of breath as you meditate on the scripture. If the flow of your breathing does not match the way we've divided the verse, feel free to do what works best for you.

JOY COMES
with the morning

PSALM 30:5

As you pray with the brief scripture passage above, inhale God's love and the gift of today...and then exhale your control, releasing all back to God. Continue to prayerfully breathe the scripture in and out for a few minutes before you proceed on to the journaling page.

Please note that since we've used both the NRSV and the NAB translations, what you see on these pages may not always match what is in your Bible.

THE JOURNALING PAGE:

Modeled directly after the Morning Offering prayer, the next section of each daily entry features an opportunity to write down the prayers of your heart. Each of the five journaling questions explores a different aspect of your day through the lenses of thanksgiving and petition.

As I rise to begin the day, Jesus, these thoughts fill my mind...

This section provides a space to take whatever is currently on your heart in the morning and lay it before the Lord. Now is the time to empty yourself to make room for Him to move in your mind, body, and spirit throughout the rest of your day.

When I gaze into your Sacred Heart, these prayers surface in my heart...

In this section, take a moment to share with God the deepest longings of your heart and the desires of those you love. He hears your requests and will respond with love. Do not hesitate to humbly ask Him for what you want or need.

As I look to the day ahead, I offer these plans and tasks from my to-do list to you...

No matter how big or small the tasks of the upcoming day may be, pause and ask Him to order your day in His peace. Surrender each aspect of your day to Him.

My heart fills with gratitude and joy when I think of...

What blessings has God showered you with lately? How has He shown himself to be faithful? As you examine the small and large blessings of your life, feel free to use this section to praise Him for His goodness.

Jesus, help me to surrender these concerns and crosses to you...

He waits for you with open arms, grace and mercy flowing forth from His pierced side. Whatever burdens you carry, take a moment to offer them to Him.

Finally, the bottom of each journaling page ends with a simple, heartfelt prayer: *I offer all this to you, my Jesus. Draw me ever closer to your Sacred Heart today. Allow me to rest in you. Amen.*

If you find you would like some advice, at the end of the journal, we have included a section titled "Additional Guidance." This section takes the format of a guided meditation and unpacks the journaling page by including more detailed questions for you to ponder.

EXTRAS:

We've designed this journal to be of service to you on your unique spiritual journey. In order to walk more intentionally with you and to provide you with additional direction, we've included a few extra pages.

At both the beginning and the end of the journal, you'll find a section titled "Reflecting On My Morning." These extra journaling assessments will provide you with the opportunity to reflect on your morning routine both before starting and after finishing this journal. Be honest in your responses. Above all else, know that God longs for the fullness of your heart given to Him.

At the end of the journal, you'll also note a section titled "My Morning Offering." Should you desire, this is a space to write your own morning offering. Speaking to God candidly in your own voice is a beautiful experience. When you take the time to offer yourself wholeheartedly to God in your own words, often you will feel empowered to persevere in this spiritual practice of morning prayer.

WHY SHOULD I USE THIS JOURNAL?

The Morning Offering Journal allows you to reclaim your day by giving it away. God gives us each the ability to freely choose the good and the holy; He gifts us control of our own actions. Today, and each day, we have the ability to begin our day by reorienting our hearts towards Him. When we decide to begin the morning in a posture of worship, we can more easily rest in the knowledge that God is in charge of whatever the day ahead holds. We need not fear; He holds us continually in His love.

When we surrender our days to God through this journal, our first thoughts at the break of a new day rest upon Him. Humbly, we approach the throne of mercy and ask Him to order our days and our hearts in His peace, according to His will, rather than our own.

Each morning wipes the slate clean and provides us with another chance to begin anew, to lean into the Father's love and mercy for us on THIS day. Regardless of the triumphs and failures of yesterday, every morning is a beautiful gift where we can once again turn towards God and offer Him all. It is important to remember that there is no failure, only the constant opportunity to return to Him with renewed courage and commitment.

Our deepest calling as Christians is to become saints. For those who long to fulfill this calling, utilizing this journal on a regular basis will nurture a healthy habit based on a tried and true spiritual practice. As our perseverance in this habit increases, we will continue to grow in virtue.

The Catechism of the Catholic Church exhorts us to pursue holiness daily by reminding us of the power of dedicating each moment to our Heavenly Father:

"The Christian begins his day, his prayers, and his activities with the Sign of the Cross: "in the name of the Father and of the Son and of the Holy Spirit. Amen." The baptized person dedicates the day to the glory of God and calls on the Savior's grace which lets him act in the Spirit as a child of the Father." (CCC 2157)

And so, today, dear friend, we begin anew. We fall into His embrace and surrender to Him each moment of the day that lies ahead. Let us join hands and walk together on this journey towards heaven.

HOW SHOULD I USE THIS JOURNAL?

This journal is meant to be a simple activity, not a burdensome chore. As you examine all of the day's tasks, intentions, worries and excitement before it begins, know that there is no set time limit. You can spend as much or as little time reflecting with God as you would like.

Do not worry about writing a pristine, perfect entry. This journal is meant to provide space for you to share honestly with God and hear Him speaking lovingly to you in return. Take comfort in the fact that no matter how fancy your handwriting is or how perfectly you compose your words, it truly does not matter to Him.

Whether you choose to keep the Morning Offering Journal on your nightstand and journal upon waking or elect to pray over these pages during your first daily sips of coffee, rest in the knowledge that God is with you. Begin each day by asking Him to guide you, both as you journal and as you enter into the rest of your day.

As the edges of your journaling pages become progressively more creased, we pray that the light of Christ will illuminate your heart more fully each and every day.

He is waiting you, dear friend. He is waiting for you with wide open arms.

Let us entrust ourselves into His loving care and begin this day anew, step in step with Him.

Let us reclaim our days by giving them away.

reflecting
on my morning
part one

We invite you to take a few minutes to reflect on your current morning routine before you begin this journal. There are no right or wrong answers. Regardless of where you are at in your spiritual journey, this reflection simply provides the opportunity to come humbly before Him and invite Him into your days.

Three words that describe how I feel upon waking are...

pressure
grateful for sleep
brief peace

My morning routine currently consists of...

Bible
writing
prayer
water

After my morning routine, I feel...

prepared for the day
tuned up with God

Ideally, after my morning routine, I'd like to feel...

like I connected with God
that I made writing progress

I am currently inviting God into my day each morning by...

reading the Bible
prayer

One way I could more fully invite God into my day is by...

Spending more time connecting

Other than using this journal, some other ideas to help me to begin my day more peacefully are (examples: lighting a candle, setting up my coffee maker the night before, waking up 10 minutes earlier, etc.)...

cleaning at night? Not sure that would
do the intended

the MORNING OFFERING *journal*

JOY COMES
with the morning

PSALM 30:5

As I rise to begin the day, Jesus, these thoughts fill my mind...

It's the best time of the day
I have to work today
I need another job to pay bills
I want to write

When I gaze into your Sacred Heart, these prayers surface in my heart...

Please work out the details of my day, it can be overwhelming. Please fine-tune my children and my marriage to be responsive to you. Please keep us close to our friends

As I look to the day ahead, I offer these plans and tasks on my to-do list to you...

work   chores
writing   alone time
cleaning
planning school
cooking

My heart fills with gratitude and joy when I think of...

time alone
seeing my friend
your future plans
your constant care for me

Jesus, help me to surrender these concerns and crosses to you...

anxiety over money
alone time
shopping
organizing the camping trip

I offer this all to you, my Jesus. Draw me ever closer to your Sacred Heart today. Allow me to rest in you. Amen.

BE STILL

and know

PSALM 46:10

_____ / _____ / _____

As I rise to begin the day, Jesus, these thoughts fill my mind...

_____
_____
_____
_____
_____

When I gaze into your Sacred Heart, these prayers surface in my heart...

_____
_____
_____
_____
_____

As I look to the day ahead, I offer these plans and tasks on my to-do list to you...

_____
_____
_____
_____
_____

My heart fills with gratitude and joy when I think of...

_____
_____
_____
_____
_____

Jesus, help me to surrender these concerns and crosses to you...

_____
_____
_____
_____
_____

I offer this all to you, my Jesus. Draw me ever closer
to your Sacred Heart today. Allow me to rest in you. Amen.

THIS IS THE DAY

that

the Lord

has made

PSALM 118:24

_____/_____/_____

As I rise to begin the day, Jesus, these thoughts fill my mind...

_____
_____
_____
_____
_____

When I gaze into your Sacred Heart, these prayers surface in my heart...

_____
_____
_____
_____
_____

As I look to the day ahead, I offer these plans and tasks on my to-do list to you...

_____
_____
_____
_____
_____

My heart fills with gratitude and joy when I think of...

_____
_____
_____
_____
_____

Jesus, help me to surrender these concerns and crosses to you...

_____
_____
_____
_____
_____

I offer this all to you, my Jesus. Draw me ever closer
to your Sacred Heart today. Allow me to rest in you. Amen.

YOU ARE BEAUTIFUL

my love

SONG OF SOLOMON 1:15

As I rise to begin the day, Jesus, these thoughts fill my mind...

_____
_____
_____
_____
_____

When I gaze into your Sacred Heart, these prayers surface in my heart...

_____
_____
_____
_____
_____

As I look to the day ahead, I offer these plans and tasks on my to-do list to you...

_____
_____
_____
_____
_____

My heart fills with gratitude and joy when I think of...

_____
_____
_____
_____
_____

Jesus, help me to surrender these concerns and crosses to you...

_____
_____
_____
_____
_____

I offer this all to you, my Jesus. Draw me ever closer
to your Sacred Heart today. Allow me to rest in you. Amen.

FOR GOD

all things

are possible

MATTHEW 19:26

_____ / _____ / _____

As I rise to begin the day, Jesus, these thoughts fill my mind...

_____
_____
_____
_____
_____

When I gaze into your Sacred Heart, these prayers surface in my heart...

_____
_____
_____
_____
_____

As I look to the day ahead, I offer these plans and tasks on my to-do list to you...

_____
_____
_____
_____
_____

My heart fills with gratitude and joy when I think of...

_____
_____
_____
_____
_____

Jesus, help me to surrender these concerns and crosses to you...

_____
_____
_____
_____
_____

I offer this all to you, my Jesus. Draw me ever closer
to your Sacred Heart today. Allow me to rest in you. Amen.

CREATE IN ME
a clean heart

PSALM 51:10

As I rise to begin the day, Jesus, these thoughts fill my mind...

_____
_____
_____
_____
_____

When I gaze into your Sacred Heart, these prayers surface in my heart...

_____
_____
_____
_____
_____

As I look to the day ahead, I offer these plans and tasks on my to-do list to you...

_____
_____
_____
_____
_____

My heart fills with gratitude and joy when I think of...

_____
_____
_____
_____
_____

Jesus, help me to surrender these concerns and crosses to you...

_____
_____
_____
_____
_____

I offer this all to you, my Jesus. Draw me ever closer
to your Sacred Heart today. Allow me to rest in you. Amen.

STRIVE FIRST
for the kingdom

MATTHEW 6:33

_____/_____/_____

As I rise to begin the day, Jesus, these thoughts fill my mind...

_____
_____
_____
_____
_____

When I gaze into your Sacred Heart, these prayers surface in my heart...

_____
_____
_____
_____
_____

As I look to the day ahead, I offer these plans and tasks on my to-do list to you...

_____
_____
_____
_____
_____

My heart fills with gratitude and joy when I think of...

_____
_____
_____
_____
_____

Jesus, help me to surrender these concerns and crosses to you...

_____
_____
_____
_____
_____

I offer this all to you, my Jesus. Draw me ever closer
to your Sacred Heart today. Allow me to rest in you. Amen.

MY SPIRIT REJOICES

in God my Savior

LUKE 1:47

As I rise to begin the day, Jesus, these thoughts fill my mind...

_____
_____
_____
_____
_____

When I gaze into your Sacred Heart, these prayers surface in my heart...

_____
_____
_____
_____
_____

As I look to the day ahead, I offer these plans and tasks on my to-do list to you...

_____
_____
_____
_____
_____

My heart fills with gratitude and joy when I think of...

_____
_____
_____
_____
_____

Jesus, help me to surrender these concerns and crosses to you...

_____
_____
_____
_____
_____

I offer this all to you, my Jesus. Draw me ever closer
to your Sacred Heart today. Allow me to rest in you. Amen.

I AM WITH YOU

always

MATTHEW 28:20

_____/_____/_____

As I rise to begin the day, Jesus, these thoughts fill my mind...

_____
_____
_____
_____
_____

When I gaze into your Sacred Heart, these prayers surface in my heart...

_____
_____
_____
_____
_____

As I look to the day ahead, I offer these plans and tasks on my to-do list to you...

_____
_____
_____
_____
_____

My heart fills with gratitude and joy when I think of...

_____
_____
_____
_____
_____

Jesus, help me to surrender these concerns and crosses to you...

_____
_____
_____
_____
_____

I offer this all to you, my Jesus. Draw me ever closer
to your Sacred Heart today. Allow me to rest in you. Amen.

YOU ARE THE LIGHT
of the world

MATTHEW 5:14

As I rise to begin the day, Jesus, these thoughts fill my mind...

_____
_____
_____
_____
_____

When I gaze into your Sacred Heart, these prayers surface in my heart...

_____
_____
_____
_____
_____

As I look to the day ahead, I offer these plans and tasks on my to-do list to you...

_____
_____
_____
_____
_____

My heart fills with gratitude and joy when I think of...

_____
_____
_____
_____

Jesus, help me to surrender these concerns and crosses to you...

_____
_____
_____
_____
_____

I offer this all to you, my Jesus. Draw me ever closer
to your Sacred Heart today. Allow me to rest in you. Amen.

WALK BY FAITH

not by sight

2 CORINTHIANS 5:7

_____ / _____ / _____

As I rise to begin the day, Jesus, these thoughts fill my mind...

_____
_____
_____
_____
_____

When I gaze into your Sacred Heart, these prayers surface in my heart...

_____
_____
_____
_____
_____

As I look to the day ahead, I offer these plans and tasks on my to-do list to you...

_____
_____
_____
_____
_____

My heart fills with gratitude and joy when I think of...

_____
_____
_____
_____
_____

Jesus, help me to surrender these concerns and crosses to you...

_____
_____
_____
_____
_____

I offer this all to you, my Jesus. Draw me ever closer
to your Sacred Heart today. Allow me to rest in you. Amen.

GIVE THANKS
TO THE LORD
for He is good

PSALM 136:1

_____/_____/_____

As I rise to begin the day, Jesus, these thoughts fill my mind...

_____
_____
_____
_____
_____

When I gaze into your Sacred Heart, these prayers surface in my heart...

_____
_____
_____
_____
_____

As I look to the day ahead, I offer these plans and tasks on my to-do list to you...

_____
_____
_____
_____
_____

My heart fills with gratitude and joy when I think of...

_____
_____
_____
_____
_____

Jesus, help me to surrender these concerns and crosses to you...

_____
_____
_____
_____
_____

I offer this all to you, my Jesus. Draw me ever closer
to your Sacred Heart today. Allow me to rest in you. Amen.

HIS LOVE

endures forever

PSALM 136:1

_____/_____/_____

As I rise to begin the day, Jesus, these thoughts fill my mind...

_____
_____
_____
_____
_____

When I gaze into your Sacred Heart, these prayers surface in my heart...

_____
_____
_____
_____
_____

As I look to the day ahead, I offer these plans and tasks on my to-do list to you...

_____
_____
_____
_____
_____

My heart fills with gratitude and joy when I think of...

_____
_____
_____
_____
_____

Jesus, help me to surrender these concerns and crosses to you...

_____
_____
_____
_____
_____

I offer this all to you, my Jesus. Draw me ever closer
to your Sacred Heart today. Allow me to rest in you. Amen.

WE SHOULD
BE CALLED

children

of God

1 JOHN 3:1

_____/_____/_____

As I rise to begin the day, Jesus, these thoughts fill my mind...

_____
_____
_____
_____
_____

When I gaze into your Sacred Heart, these prayers surface in my heart...

_____
_____
_____
_____
_____

As I look to the day ahead, I offer these plans and tasks on my to-do list to you...

_____
_____
_____
_____
_____

My heart fills with gratitude and joy when I think of...

_____
_____
_____
_____
_____

Jesus, help me to surrender these concerns and crosses to you...

_____
_____
_____
_____
_____

I offer this all to you, my Jesus. Draw me ever closer
to your Sacred Heart today. Allow me to rest in you. Amen.

I WILL
BLESS THE LORD

at all times

PSALM 34:1

_____ / _____ / _____

As I rise to begin the day, Jesus, these thoughts fill my mind...

_____
_____
_____
_____
_____

When I gaze into your Sacred Heart, these prayers surface in my heart...

_____
_____
_____
_____
_____

As I look to the day ahead, I offer these plans and tasks on my to-do list to you...

_____
_____
_____
_____
_____

My heart fills with gratitude and joy when I think of...

_____
_____
_____
_____
_____

Jesus, help me to surrender these concerns and crosses to you...

_____
_____
_____
_____
_____

I offer this all to you, my Jesus. Draw me ever closer
to your Sacred Heart today. Allow me to rest in you. Amen.

HIS MERCIES
ARE NEW

---

every morning

LAMENTATIONS 3:22-23

_____/_____/_____

As I rise to begin the day, Jesus, these thoughts fill my mind...

_____
_____
_____
_____
_____

When I gaze into your Sacred Heart, these prayers surface in my heart...

_____
_____
_____
_____
_____

As I look to the day ahead, I offer these plans and tasks on my to-do list to you...

_____
_____
_____
_____
_____

My heart fills with gratitude and joy when I think of...

_____
_____
_____
_____
_____

Jesus, help me to surrender these concerns and crosses to you...

_____
_____
_____
_____
_____

I offer this all to you, my Jesus. Draw me ever closer
to your Sacred Heart today. Allow me to rest in you. Amen.

GRACE

upon grace

JOHN 1:16

____/____/____

As I rise to begin the day, Jesus, these thoughts fill my mind...

_____
_____
_____
_____
_____

When I gaze into your Sacred Heart, these prayers surface in my heart...

_____
_____
_____
_____
_____

As I look to the day ahead, I offer these plans and tasks on my to-do list to you...

_____
_____
_____
_____
_____

My heart fills with gratitude and joy when I think of...

_____
_____
_____
_____
_____

Jesus, help me to surrender these concerns and crosses to you...

_____
_____
_____
_____
_____

I offer this all to you, my Jesus. Draw me ever closer
to your Sacred Heart today. Allow me to rest in you. Amen.

PRAY

---

without ceasing

1 THESSALONIANS 5:17

_____/_____/_____

As I rise to begin the day, Jesus, these thoughts fill my mind...

_____
_____
_____
_____
_____

When I gaze into your Sacred Heart, these prayers surface in my heart...

_____
_____
_____
_____
_____

As I look to the day ahead, I offer these plans and tasks on my to-do list to you...

_____
_____
_____
_____
_____

My heart fills with gratitude and joy when I think of...

_____
_____
_____
_____
_____

Jesus, help me to surrender these concerns and crosses to you...

_____
_____
_____
_____
_____

I offer this all to you, my Jesus. Draw me ever closer
to your Sacred Heart today. Allow me to rest in you. Amen.

LET US REJOICE
and be glad

PSALM 118:24

_____ / _____ / _____

As I rise to begin the day, Jesus, these thoughts fill my mind...

_____

_____

_____

_____

_____

When I gaze into your Sacred Heart, these prayers surface in my heart...

_____

_____

_____

_____

_____

As I look to the day ahead, I offer these plans and tasks on my to-do list to you...

_____

_____

_____

_____

_____

My heart fills with gratitude and joy when I think of...

_____

_____

_____

_____

_____

Jesus, help me to surrender these concerns and crosses to you...

_____

_____

_____

_____

_____

I offer this all to you, my Jesus. Draw me ever closer
to your Sacred Heart today. Allow me to rest in you. Amen.

I FEAR NO EVIL

for you are

with me

PSALM 23:4

____ / ____ / ____

As I rise to begin the day, Jesus, these thoughts fill my mind...

_____
_____
_____
_____
_____

When I gaze into your Sacred Heart, these prayers surface in my heart...

_____
_____
_____
_____
_____

As I look to the day ahead, I offer these plans and tasks on my to-do list to you...

_____
_____
_____
_____
_____

My heart fills with gratitude and joy when I think of...

_____
_____
_____
_____
_____

Jesus, help me to surrender these concerns and crosses to you...

_____
_____
_____
_____
_____

I offer this all to you, my Jesus. Draw me ever closer
to your Sacred Heart today. Allow me to rest in you. Amen.

GIVE THANKS

---

in all circumstances

1 THESSALONIANS 5:18

_____ / _____ / _____

As I rise to begin the day, Jesus, these thoughts fill my mind...

_____
_____
_____
_____
_____

When I gaze into your Sacred Heart, these prayers surface in my heart...

_____
_____
_____
_____
_____

As I look to the day ahead, I offer these plans and tasks on my to-do list to you...

_____
_____
_____
_____
_____

My heart fills with gratitude and joy when I think of...

_____
_____
_____
_____
_____

Jesus, help me to surrender these concerns and crosses to you...

_____
_____
_____
_____
_____

I offer this all to you, my Jesus. Draw me ever closer
to your Sacred Heart today. Allow me to rest in you. Amen.

I AM

wonderfully made

PSALM 139:14

As I rise to begin the day, Jesus, these thoughts fill my mind...

_____
_____
_____
_____
_____

When I gaze into your Sacred Heart, these prayers surface in my heart...

_____
_____
_____
_____
_____

As I look to the day ahead, I offer these plans and tasks on my to-do list to you...

_____
_____
_____
_____
_____

My heart fills with gratitude and joy when I think of...

_____
_____
_____
_____
_____

Jesus, help me to surrender these concerns and crosses to you...

_____
_____
_____
_____
_____

I offer this all to you, my Jesus. Draw me ever closer
to your Sacred Heart today. Allow me to rest in you. Amen.

DO NOT LET
YOUR HEART
be troubled

JOHN 14:1

_____/_____/_____

As I rise to begin the day, Jesus, these thoughts fill my mind...

_____
_____
_____
_____
_____

When I gaze into your Sacred Heart, these prayers surface in my heart...

_____
_____
_____
_____
_____

As I look to the day ahead, I offer these plans and tasks on my to-do list to you...

_____
_____
_____
_____
_____

My heart fills with gratitude and joy when I think of...

_____
_____
_____
_____
_____

Jesus, help me to surrender these concerns and crosses to you...

_____
_____
_____
_____
_____

I offer this all to you, my Jesus. Draw me ever closer
to your Sacred Heart today. Allow me to rest in you. Amen.

FOR EVERYTHING

there is a season

ECCLESIASTES 3:1

_____/_____/_____

As I rise to begin the day, Jesus, these thoughts fill my mind...

_____
_____
_____
_____
_____

When I gaze into your Sacred Heart, these prayers surface in my heart...

_____
_____
_____
_____
_____

As I look to the day ahead, I offer these plans and tasks on my to-do list to you...

_____
_____
_____
_____
_____

My heart fills with gratitude and joy when I think of...

_____
_____
_____
_____
_____

Jesus, help me to surrender these concerns and crosses to you...

_____
_____
_____
_____
_____

I offer this all to you, my Jesus. Draw me ever closer
to your Sacred Heart today. Allow me to rest in you. Amen.

REJOICE

in hope

ROMANS 12:12

_____/_____/_____

As I rise to begin the day, Jesus, these thoughts fill my mind...

_____
_____
_____
_____
_____

When I gaze into your Sacred Heart, these prayers surface in my heart...

_____
_____
_____
_____
_____

As I look to the day ahead, I offer these plans and tasks on my to-do list to you...

_____
_____
_____
_____

My heart fills with gratitude and joy when I think of...

_____
_____
_____
_____
_____

Jesus, help me to surrender these concerns and crosses to you...

_____
_____
_____
_____
_____

I offer this all to you, my Jesus. Draw me ever closer
to your Sacred Heart today. Allow me to rest in you. Amen.

THE LORD IS MY SHEPHERD

I shall not want

PSALM 23:1

_____/_____/_____

As I rise to begin the day, Jesus, these thoughts fill my mind...

_____

_____

_____

_____

_____

When I gaze into your Sacred Heart, these prayers surface in my heart...

_____

_____

_____

_____

_____

As I look to the day ahead, I offer these plans and tasks on my to-do list to you...

_____

_____

_____

_____

_____

My heart fills with gratitude and joy when I think of...

_____

_____

_____

_____

_____

Jesus, help me to surrender these concerns and crosses to you...

_____

_____

_____

_____

_____

I offer this all to you, my Jesus. Draw me ever closer
to your Sacred Heart today. Allow me to rest in you. Amen.

TO YOU OH LORD

I lift my soul

PSALM 25:1

_____/_____/_____

As I rise to begin the day, Jesus, these thoughts fill my mind...

_____
_____
_____
_____
_____

When I gaze into your Sacred Heart, these prayers surface in my heart...

_____
_____
_____
_____
_____

As I look to the day ahead, I offer these plans and tasks on my to-do list to you...

_____
_____
_____
_____
_____

My heart fills with gratitude and joy when I think of...

_____
_____
_____
_____
_____

Jesus, help me to surrender these concerns and crosses to you...

_____
_____
_____
_____
_____

I offer this all to you, my Jesus. Draw me ever closer
to your Sacred Heart today. Allow me to rest in you. Amen.

SEEK THE LORD

and his strength

1 CHRONICLES 16:11

_____/_____/_____

As I rise to begin the day, Jesus, these thoughts fill my mind...

_____
_____
_____
_____
_____

When I gaze into your Sacred Heart, these prayers surface in my heart...

_____
_____
_____
_____
_____

As I look to the day ahead, I offer these plans and tasks on my to-do list to you...

_____
_____
_____
_____
_____

My heart fills with gratitude and joy when I think of...

_____
_____
_____
_____
_____

Jesus, help me to surrender these concerns and crosses to you...

_____
_____
_____
_____
_____

I offer this all to you, my Jesus. Draw me ever closer
to your Sacred Heart today. Allow me to rest in you. Amen.

SET YOUR MIND

on things that are above

COLOSSIANS 3:2

As I rise to begin the day, Jesus, these thoughts fill my mind...

_____
_____
_____
_____
_____

When I gaze into your Sacred Heart, these prayers surface in my heart...

_____
_____
_____
_____
_____

As I look to the day ahead, I offer these plans and tasks on my to-do list to you...

_____
_____
_____
_____
_____

My heart fills with gratitude and joy when I think of...

_____
_____
_____
_____
_____

Jesus, help me to surrender these concerns and crosses to you...

_____
_____
_____
_____
_____

I offer this all to you, my Jesus. Draw me ever closer
to your Sacred Heart today. Allow me to rest in you. Amen.

TRUST IN THE LORD

with all your heart

PROVERBS 3:5

_____/_____/_____

As I rise to begin the day, Jesus, these thoughts fill my mind...

_____
_____
_____
_____
_____

When I gaze into your Sacred Heart, these prayers surface in my heart...

_____
_____
_____
_____
_____

As I look to the day ahead, I offer these plans and tasks on my to-do list to you...

_____
_____
_____
_____
_____

My heart fills with gratitude and joy when I think of...

_____
_____
_____
_____
_____

Jesus, help me to surrender these concerns and crosses to you...

_____
_____
_____
_____
_____

I offer this all to you, my Jesus. Draw me ever closer
to your Sacred Heart today. Allow me to rest in you. Amen.

TAKE DELIGHT

---

in the Lord

PSALM 37:4

_____ / _____ / _____

As I rise to begin the day, Jesus, these thoughts fill my mind...

_____
_____
_____
_____
_____

When I gaze into your Sacred Heart, these prayers surface in my heart...

_____
_____
_____
_____
_____

As I look to the day ahead, I offer these plans and tasks on my to-do list to you...

_____
_____
_____
_____
_____

My heart fills with gratitude and joy when I think of...

_____
_____
_____
_____

Jesus, help me to surrender these concerns and crosses to you...

_____
_____
_____
_____

I offer this all to you, my Jesus. Draw me ever closer
to your Sacred Heart today. Allow me to rest in you. Amen.

WE LOVE

because He first loved us

1 JOHN 4:19

As I rise to begin the day, Jesus, these thoughts fill my mind...

_____
_____
_____
_____
_____

When I gaze into your Sacred Heart, these prayers surface in my heart...

_____
_____
_____
_____
_____

As I look to the day ahead, I offer these plans and tasks on my to-do list to you...

_____
_____
_____
_____
_____

My heart fills with gratitude and joy when I think of...

_____
_____
_____
_____
_____

Jesus, help me to surrender these concerns and crosses to you...

_____
_____
_____
_____
_____

I offer this all to you, my Jesus. Draw me ever closer
to your Sacred Heart today. Allow me to rest in you. Amen.

I CAN DO
ALL THINGS
through Him

PHILIPPIANS 4:13

_____/_____/_____

As I rise to begin the day, Jesus, these thoughts fill my mind...

_____
_____
_____
_____
_____

When I gaze into your Sacred Heart, these prayers surface in my heart...

_____
_____
_____
_____
_____

As I look to the day ahead, I offer these plans and tasks on my to-do list to you...

_____
_____
_____
_____
_____

My heart fills with gratitude and joy when I think of...

_____
_____
_____
_____
_____

Jesus, help me to surrender these concerns and crosses to you...

_____
_____
_____
_____

I offer this all to you, my Jesus. Draw me ever closer
to your Sacred Heart today. Allow me to rest in you. Amen.

BE PATIENT

in suffering

ROMANS 12:12

_____ / _____ / _____

As I rise to begin the day, Jesus, these thoughts fill my mind...

_____
_____
_____
_____
_____

When I gaze into your Sacred Heart, these prayers surface in my heart...

_____
_____
_____
_____
_____

As I look to the day ahead, I offer these plans and tasks on my to-do list to you...

_____
_____
_____
_____
_____

My heart fills with gratitude and joy when I think of...

_____
_____
_____
_____
_____

Jesus, help me to surrender these concerns and crosses to you...

_____
_____
_____
_____
_____

I offer this all to you, my Jesus. Draw me ever closer
to your Sacred Heart today. Allow me to rest in you. Amen.

DO EVERYTHING

for the glory of God

1 CORINTHIANS 10:31

As I rise to begin the day, Jesus, these thoughts fill my mind...

_____
_____
_____
_____
_____

When I gaze into your Sacred Heart, these prayers surface in my heart...

_____
_____
_____
_____
_____

As I look to the day ahead, I offer these plans and tasks on my to-do list to you...

_____
_____
_____
_____
_____

My heart fills with gratitude and joy when I think of...

_____
_____
_____
_____
_____

Jesus, help me to surrender these concerns and crosses to you...

_____
_____
_____
_____
_____

I offer this all to you, my Jesus. Draw me ever closer
to your Sacred Heart today. Allow me to rest in you. Amen.

ON THE DAY
I CALLED

you answered me

PSALM 138:3

_____/_____/_____

As I rise to begin the day, Jesus, these thoughts fill my mind...

_____
_____
_____
_____
_____

When I gaze into your Sacred Heart, these prayers surface in my heart...

_____
_____
_____
_____
_____

As I look to the day ahead, I offer these plans and tasks on my to-do list to you...

_____
_____
_____
_____
_____

My heart fills with gratitude and joy when I think of...

_____
_____
_____
_____
_____

Jesus, help me to surrender these concerns and crosses to you...

_____
_____
_____
_____
_____

I offer this all to you, my Jesus. Draw me ever closer
to your Sacred Heart today. Allow me to rest in you. Amen.

I WILL GIVE

you rest

MATTHEW 11:28

_____/_____/_____

As I rise to begin the day, Jesus, these thoughts fill my mind...

_____
_____
_____
_____
_____

When I gaze into your Sacred Heart, these prayers surface in my heart...

_____
_____
_____
_____
_____

As I look to the day ahead, I offer these plans and tasks on my to-do list to you...

_____
_____
_____
_____
_____

My heart fills with gratitude and joy when I think of...

_____
_____
_____
_____
_____

Jesus, help me to surrender these concerns and crosses to you...

_____
_____
_____
_____
_____

I offer this all to you, my Jesus. Draw me ever closer
to your Sacred Heart today. Allow me to rest in you. Amen.

YOU HAVE

been born anew

1 PETER 1:23

___/___/___

As I rise to begin the day, Jesus, these thoughts fill my mind...

_____
_____
_____
_____
_____

When I gaze into your Sacred Heart, these prayers surface in my heart...

_____
_____
_____
_____
_____

As I look to the day ahead, I offer these plans and tasks on my to-do list to you...

_____
_____
_____
_____
_____

My heart fills with gratitude and joy when I think of...

_____
_____
_____
_____
_____

Jesus, help me to surrender these concerns and crosses to you...

_____
_____
_____
_____
_____

I offer this all to you, my Jesus. Draw me ever closer
to your Sacred Heart today. Allow me to rest in you. Amen.

AND THE GREATEST

---

is love

1 CORINTHIANS 13:13

_____/_____/_____

As I rise to begin the day, Jesus, these thoughts fill my mind...

_____
_____
_____
_____
_____

When I gaze into your Sacred Heart, these prayers surface in my heart...

_____
_____
_____
_____
_____

As I look to the day ahead, I offer these plans and tasks on my to-do list to you...

_____
_____
_____
_____
_____

My heart fills with gratitude and joy when I think of...

_____
_____
_____
_____
_____

Jesus, help me to surrender these concerns and crosses to you...

_____
_____
_____
_____
_____

I offer this all to you, my Jesus. Draw me ever closer
to your Sacred Heart today. Allow me to rest in you. Amen.

FOR GOD

---

so loved

the world

JOHN 3:16

_____/_____/_____

As I rise to begin the day, Jesus, these thoughts fill my mind...

_____
_____
_____
_____
_____

When I gaze into your Sacred Heart, these prayers surface in my heart...

_____
_____
_____
_____
_____

As I look to the day ahead, I offer these plans and tasks on my to-do list to you...

_____
_____
_____
_____
_____

My heart fills with gratitude and joy when I think of...

_____
_____
_____
_____
_____

Jesus, help me to surrender these concerns and crosses to you...

_____
_____
_____
_____
_____

I offer this all to you, my Jesus. Draw me ever closer
to your Sacred Heart today. Allow me to rest in you. Amen.

BE STRONG

and let your heart take courage

PSALM 31:24

_____ / _____ / _____

As I rise to begin the day, Jesus, these thoughts fill my mind...

_____
_____
_____
_____
_____

When I gaze into your Sacred Heart, these prayers surface in my heart...

_____
_____
_____
_____
_____

As I look to the day ahead, I offer these plans and tasks on my to-do list to you...

_____
_____
_____
_____
_____

My heart fills with gratitude and joy when I think of...

_____
_____
_____
_____
_____

Jesus, help me to surrender these concerns and crosses to you...

_____
_____
_____
_____
_____

I offer this all to you, my Jesus. Draw me ever closer
to your Sacred Heart today. Allow me to rest in you. Amen.

DO WHATEVER
he tells you

JOHN 2:5

_____/_____/_____

As I rise to begin the day, Jesus, these thoughts fill my mind...

_____
_____
_____
_____
_____

When I gaze into your Sacred Heart, these prayers surface in my heart...

_____
_____
_____
_____
_____

As I look to the day ahead, I offer these plans and tasks on my to-do list to you...

_____
_____
_____
_____
_____

My heart fills with gratitude and joy when I think of...

_____
_____
_____
_____
_____

Jesus, help me to surrender these concerns and crosses to you...

_____
_____
_____
_____
_____

I offer this all to you, my Jesus. Draw me ever closer
to your Sacred Heart today. Allow me to rest in you. Amen.

YOUR LIGHT
MUST SHINE

before others

MATTHEW 5:16

As I rise to begin the day, Jesus, these thoughts fill my mind...

_____
_____
_____
_____
_____

When I gaze into your Sacred Heart, these prayers surface in my heart...

_____
_____
_____
_____
_____

As I look to the day ahead, I offer these plans and tasks on my to-do list to you...

_____
_____
_____
_____
_____

My heart fills with gratitude and joy when I think of...

_____
_____
_____
_____
_____

Jesus, help me to surrender these concerns and crosses to you...

_____
_____
_____
_____
_____

I offer this all to you, my Jesus. Draw me ever closer
to your Sacred Heart today. Allow me to rest in you. Amen.

PERSEVERE

in prayer

ROMANS 12:12

As I rise to begin the day, Jesus, these thoughts fill my mind...

_____

_____

_____

_____

_____

When I gaze into your Sacred Heart, these prayers surface in my heart...

_____

_____

_____

_____

_____

As I look to the day ahead, I offer these plans and tasks on my to-do list to you...

_____

_____

_____

_____

_____

My heart fills with gratitude and joy when I think of...

_____

_____

_____

_____

_____

Jesus, help me to surrender these concerns and crosses to you...

_____

_____

_____

_____

_____

I offer this all to you, my Jesus. Draw me ever closer
to your Sacred Heart today. Allow me to rest in you. Amen.

FOR GOD ALONE

my soul waits

in courage

PSALM 62:5

_____/_____/_____

As I rise to begin the day, Jesus, these thoughts fill my mind...

_____
_____
_____
_____
_____

When I gaze into your Sacred Heart, these prayers surface in my heart...

_____
_____
_____
_____
_____

As I look to the day ahead, I offer these plans and tasks on my to-do list to you...

_____
_____
_____
_____
_____

My heart fills with gratitude and joy when I think of...

_____
_____
_____
_____
_____

Jesus, help me to surrender these concerns and crosses to you...

_____
_____
_____
_____
_____

I offer this all to you, my Jesus. Draw me ever closer
to your Sacred Heart today. Allow me to rest in you. Amen.

THE LORD IS

merciful and gracious

PSALM 103:8

____/____/____

As I rise to begin the day, Jesus, these thoughts fill my mind...

_____

_____

_____

_____

_____

When I gaze into your Sacred Heart, these prayers surface in my heart...

_____

_____

_____

_____

_____

As I look to the day ahead, I offer these plans and tasks on my to-do list to you...

_____

_____

_____

_____

_____

My heart fills with gratitude and joy when I think of...

_____

_____

_____

_____

_____

Jesus, help me to surrender these concerns and crosses to you...

_____

_____

_____

_____

_____

I offer this all to you, my Jesus. Draw me ever closer
to your Sacred Heart today. Allow me to rest in you. Amen.

MY GOD

in whom I trust

PSALM 91:2

As I rise to begin the day, Jesus, these thoughts fill my mind...

_____
_____
_____
_____
_____

When I gaze into your Sacred Heart, these prayers surface in my heart...

_____
_____
_____
_____
_____

As I look to the day ahead, I offer these plans and tasks on my to-do list to you...

_____
_____
_____
_____
_____

My heart fills with gratitude and joy when I think of...

_____
_____
_____
_____
_____

Jesus, help me to surrender these concerns and crosses to you...

_____
_____
_____
_____
_____

I offer this all to you, my Jesus. Draw me ever closer
to your Sacred Heart today. Allow me to rest in you. Amen.

I WILL PRAISE

your name

forever

PSALM 145:1

As I rise to begin the day, Jesus, these thoughts fill my mind...

_____
_____
_____
_____
_____

When I gaze into your Sacred Heart, these prayers surface in my heart...

_____
_____
_____
_____
_____

As I look to the day ahead, I offer these plans and tasks on my to-do list to you...

_____
_____
_____
_____
_____

My heart fills with gratitude and joy when I think of...

_____
_____
_____
_____
_____

Jesus, help me to surrender these concerns and crosses to you...

_____
_____
_____
_____
_____

I offer this all to you, my Jesus. Draw me ever closer
to your Sacred Heart today. Allow me to rest in you. Amen.

SPEAK LORD

your servant is listening

1 SAMUEL 3:9

_____/_____/_____

As I rise to begin the day, Jesus, these thoughts fill my mind...

_____
_____
_____
_____
_____

When I gaze into your Sacred Heart, these prayers surface in my heart...

_____
_____
_____
_____
_____

As I look to the day ahead, I offer these plans and tasks on my to-do list to you...

_____
_____
_____
_____
_____

My heart fills with gratitude and joy when I think of...

_____
_____
_____
_____
_____

Jesus, help me to surrender these concerns and crosses to you...

_____
_____
_____
_____
_____

I offer this all to you, my Jesus. Draw me ever closer
to your Sacred Heart today. Allow me to rest in you. Amen.

LIFT UP YOUR VOICE

with strength

ISAIAH 40:9

As I rise to begin the day, Jesus, these thoughts fill my mind...

_____

_____

_____

_____

_____

When I gaze into your Sacred Heart, these prayers surface in my heart...

_____

_____

_____

_____

_____

As I look to the day ahead, I offer these plans and tasks on my to-do list to you...

_____

_____

_____

_____

_____

My heart fills with gratitude and joy when I think of...

_____

_____

_____

_____

_____

Jesus, help me to surrender these concerns and crosses to you...

_____

_____

_____

_____

_____

I offer this all to you, my Jesus. Draw me ever closer
to your Sacred Heart today. Allow me to rest in you. Amen.

I AM WITH YOU

to deliver you

JEREMIAH 1:19

_____/_____/_____

As I rise to begin the day, Jesus, these thoughts fill my mind...

_____
_____
_____
_____
_____

When I gaze into your Sacred Heart, these prayers surface in my heart...

_____
_____
_____
_____
_____

As I look to the day ahead, I offer these plans and tasks on my to-do list to you...

_____
_____
_____
_____
_____

My heart fills with gratitude and joy when I think of...

_____
_____
_____
_____
_____

Jesus, help me to surrender these concerns and crosses to you...

_____
_____
_____
_____
_____

I offer this all to you, my Jesus. Draw me ever closer
to your Sacred Heart today. Allow me to rest in you. Amen.

IT IS THE SPIRIT
that gives life

JOHN 6:63

As I rise to begin the day, Jesus, these thoughts fill my mind...

_____
_____
_____
_____
_____

When I gaze into your Sacred Heart, these prayers surface in my heart...

_____
_____
_____
_____
_____

As I look to the day ahead, I offer these plans and tasks on my to-do list to you...

_____
_____
_____
_____
_____

My heart fills with gratitude and joy when I think of...

_____
_____
_____
_____
_____

Jesus, help me to surrender these concerns and crosses to you...

_____
_____
_____
_____
_____

I offer this all to you, my Jesus. Draw me ever closer
to your Sacred Heart today. Allow me to rest in you. Amen.

REJOICE

always

1 THESSALONIANS 5:16

As I rise to begin the day, Jesus, these thoughts fill my mind...

_____

_____

_____

_____

_____

When I gaze into your Sacred Heart, these prayers surface in my heart...

_____

_____

_____

_____

_____

As I look to the day ahead, I offer these plans and tasks on my to-do list to you...

_____

_____

_____

_____

_____

My heart fills with gratitude and joy when I think of...

_____

_____

_____

_____

_____

Jesus, help me to surrender these concerns and crosses to you...

_____

_____

_____

_____

_____

I offer this all to you, my Jesus. Draw me ever closer
to your Sacred Heart today. Allow me to rest in you. Amen.

YOUR WORD

is a light to my path

PSALM 119:105

_____/_____/_____

As I rise to begin the day, Jesus, these thoughts fill my mind...

_____
_____
_____
_____
_____

When I gaze into your Sacred Heart, these prayers surface in my heart...

_____
_____
_____
_____
_____

As I look to the day ahead, I offer these plans and tasks on my to-do list to you...

_____
_____
_____
_____

My heart fills with gratitude and joy when I think of...

_____
_____
_____
_____

Jesus, help me to surrender these concerns and crosses to you...

_____
_____
_____
_____

I offer this all to you, my Jesus. Draw me ever closer
to your Sacred Heart today. Allow me to rest in you. Amen.

THEY SHALL RUN

and not grow

weary

ISAIAH 40:31

_____ / _____ / _____

As I rise to begin the day, Jesus, these thoughts fill my mind...

_____
_____
_____
_____
_____

When I gaze into your Sacred Heart, these prayers surface in my heart...

_____
_____
_____
_____
_____

As I look to the day ahead, I offer these plans and tasks on my to-do list to you...

_____
_____
_____
_____
_____

My heart fills with gratitude and joy when I think of...

_____
_____
_____
_____
_____

Jesus, help me to surrender these concerns and crosses to you...

_____
_____
_____
_____
_____

I offer this all to you, my Jesus. Draw me ever closer
to your Sacred Heart today. Allow me to rest in you. Amen.

GOD IS

our refuge and strength

PSALM 46:1

_____/_____/_____

As I rise to begin the day, Jesus, these thoughts fill my mind...

_____
_____
_____
_____
_____

When I gaze into your Sacred Heart, these prayers surface in my heart...

_____
_____
_____
_____
_____

As I look to the day ahead, I offer these plans and tasks on my to-do list to you...

_____
_____
_____
_____
_____

My heart fills with gratitude and joy when I think of...

_____
_____
_____
_____
_____

Jesus, help me to surrender these concerns and crosses to you...

_____
_____
_____
_____
_____

I offer this all to you, my Jesus. Draw me ever closer
to your Sacred Heart today. Allow me to rest in you. Amen.

EVERYTHING

has become new

2 CORINTHIANS 5:17

As I rise to begin the day, Jesus, these thoughts fill my mind...

_____
_____
_____
_____
_____

When I gaze into your Sacred Heart, these prayers surface in my heart...

_____
_____
_____
_____
_____

As I look to the day ahead, I offer these plans and tasks on my to-do list to you...

_____
_____
_____
_____
_____

My heart fills with gratitude and joy when I think of...

_____
_____
_____
_____

Jesus, help me to surrender these concerns and crosses to you...

_____
_____
_____
_____

I offer this all to you, my Jesus. Draw me ever closer
to your Sacred Heart today. Allow me to rest in you. Amen.

THE SPIRIT OF GOD

dwells in you

ROMANS 8:9

_____ / _____ / _____

As I rise to begin the day, Jesus, these thoughts fill my mind...

_____
_____
_____
_____
_____

When I gaze into your Sacred Heart, these prayers surface in my heart...

_____
_____
_____
_____
_____

As I look to the day ahead, I offer these plans and tasks on my to-do list to you...

_____
_____
_____
_____
_____

My heart fills with gratitude and joy when I think of...

_____
_____
_____
_____
_____

Jesus, help me to surrender these concerns and crosses to you...

_____
_____
_____
_____
_____

I offer this all to you, my Jesus. Draw me ever closer
to your Sacred Heart today. Allow me to rest in you. Amen.

WAIT FOR

the Lord

PSALM 27:14

As I rise to begin the day, Jesus, these thoughts fill my mind...

_____

_____

_____

_____

_____

When I gaze into your Sacred Heart, these prayers surface in my heart...

_____

_____

_____

_____

_____

As I look to the day ahead, I offer these plans and tasks on my to-do list to you...

_____

_____

_____

_____

_____

My heart fills with gratitude and joy when I think of...

_____

_____

_____

_____

_____

Jesus, help me to surrender these concerns and crosses to you...

_____

_____

_____

_____

_____

I offer this all to you, my Jesus. Draw me ever closer
to your Sacred Heart today. Allow me to rest in you. Amen.

THE LORD
SHALL RENEW

their strength

ISAIAH 40:31

_____/_____/_____

As I rise to begin the day, Jesus, these thoughts fill my mind...

_____
_____
_____
_____
_____

When I gaze into your Sacred Heart, these prayers surface in my heart...

_____
_____
_____
_____
_____

As I look to the day ahead, I offer these plans and tasks on my to-do list to you...

_____
_____
_____
_____
_____

My heart fills with gratitude and joy when I think of...

_____
_____
_____
_____
_____

Jesus, help me to surrender these concerns and crosses to you...

_____
_____
_____
_____
_____

I offer this all to you, my Jesus. Draw me ever closer
to your Sacred Heart today. Allow me to rest in you. Amen.

MAKE ME TO KNOW

your ways,
O Lord

PSALM 25:4

_____ / _____ / _____

As I rise to begin the day, Jesus, these thoughts fill my mind...

_____

_____

_____

_____

_____

When I gaze into your Sacred Heart, these prayers surface in my heart...

_____

_____

_____

_____

_____

As I look to the day ahead, I offer these plans and tasks on my to-do list to you...

_____

_____

_____

_____

_____

My heart fills with gratitude and joy when I think of...

_____

_____

_____

_____

_____

Jesus, help me to surrender these concerns and crosses to you...

_____

_____

_____

_____

_____

I offer this all to you, my Jesus. Draw me ever closer
to your Sacred Heart today. Allow me to rest in you. Amen.

PREPARE THE WAY
OF THE LORD

make His
paths straight

MARK 1:3

_____ / _____ / _____

As I rise to begin the day, Jesus, these thoughts fill my mind...

_____
_____
_____
_____
_____

When I gaze into your Sacred Heart, these prayers surface in my heart...

_____
_____
_____
_____
_____

As I look to the day ahead, I offer these plans and tasks on my to-do list to you...

_____
_____
_____
_____
_____

My heart fills with gratitude and joy when I think of...

_____
_____
_____
_____
_____

Jesus, help me to surrender these concerns and crosses to you...

_____
_____
_____
_____
_____

I offer this all to you, my Jesus. Draw me ever closer
to your Sacred Heart today. Allow me to rest in you. Amen.

THE LORD

is near

PHILIPPIANS 4:5

As I rise to begin the day, Jesus, these thoughts fill my mind...

_____
_____
_____
_____
_____

When I gaze into your Sacred Heart, these prayers surface in my heart...

_____
_____
_____
_____
_____

As I look to the day ahead, I offer these plans and tasks on my to-do list to you...

_____
_____
_____
_____
_____

My heart fills with gratitude and joy when I think of...

_____
_____
_____
_____
_____

Jesus, help me to surrender these concerns and crosses to you...

_____
_____
_____
_____
_____

I offer this all to you, my Jesus. Draw me ever closer
to your Sacred Heart today. Allow me to rest in you. Amen.

HOW LOVELY IS

your dwelling place

PSALM 84:1

_____ / _____ / _____

As I rise to begin the day, Jesus, these thoughts fill my mind...

_____
_____
_____
_____
_____

When I gaze into your Sacred Heart, these prayers surface in my heart...

_____
_____
_____
_____
_____

As I look to the day ahead, I offer these plans and tasks on my to-do list to you...

_____
_____
_____
_____
_____

My heart fills with gratitude and joy when I think of...

_____
_____
_____
_____
_____

Jesus, help me to surrender these concerns and crosses to you...

_____
_____
_____
_____
_____

I offer this all to you, my Jesus. Draw me ever closer
to your Sacred Heart today. Allow me to rest in you. Amen.

LET THE PEACE
OF CHRIST

rule in your

hearts

COLOSSIANS 3:15

_____/_____/_____

As I rise to begin the day, Jesus, these thoughts fill my mind...

_____
_____
_____
_____
_____

When I gaze into your Sacred Heart, these prayers surface in my heart...

_____
_____
_____
_____
_____

As I look to the day ahead, I offer these plans and tasks on my to-do list to you...

_____
_____
_____
_____
_____

My heart fills with gratitude and joy when I think of...

_____
_____
_____
_____
_____

Jesus, help me to surrender these concerns and crosses to you...

_____
_____
_____
_____
_____

I offer this all to you, my Jesus. Draw me ever closer
to your Sacred Heart today. Allow me to rest in you. Amen.

LET THE WORD
OF CHRIST

dwell in you

COLOSSIANS 3:16

As I rise to begin the day, Jesus, these thoughts fill my mind...

_____
_____
_____
_____
_____

When I gaze into your Sacred Heart, these prayers surface in my heart...

_____
_____
_____
_____
_____

As I look to the day ahead, I offer these plans and tasks on my to-do list to you...

_____
_____
_____
_____

My heart fills with gratitude and joy when I think of...

_____
_____
_____
_____
_____

Jesus, help me to surrender these concerns and crosses to you...

_____
_____
_____
_____

I offer this all to you, my Jesus. Draw me ever closer
to your Sacred Heart today. Allow me to rest in you. Amen.

SEE WHAT LOVE

the Father

has given us

1 JOHN 3:1

As I rise to begin the day, Jesus, these thoughts fill my mind...

_____

_____

_____

_____

_____

When I gaze into your Sacred Heart, these prayers surface in my heart...

_____

_____

_____

_____

_____

As I look to the day ahead, I offer these plans and tasks on my to-do list to you...

_____

_____

_____

_____

_____

My heart fills with gratitude and joy when I think of...

_____

_____

_____

_____

_____

Jesus, help me to surrender these concerns and crosses to you...

_____

_____

_____

_____

_____

I offer this all to you, my Jesus. Draw me ever closer
to your Sacred Heart today. Allow me to rest in you. Amen.

ARISE

shine

ISAIAH 60:1

As I rise to begin the day, Jesus, these thoughts fill my mind...

_____
_____
_____
_____
_____

When I gaze into your Sacred Heart, these prayers surface in my heart...

_____
_____
_____
_____
_____

As I look to the day ahead, I offer these plans and tasks on my to-do list to you...

_____
_____
_____
_____
_____

My heart fills with gratitude and joy when I think of...

_____
_____
_____
_____
_____

Jesus, help me to surrender these concerns and crosses to you...

_____
_____
_____
_____
_____

I offer this all to you, my Jesus. Draw me ever closer
to your Sacred Heart today. Allow me to rest in you. Amen.

THE LORD
DELIGHTS

in you

ISAIAH 62:4

As I rise to begin the day, Jesus, these thoughts fill my mind...

_____
_____
_____
_____
_____

When I gaze into your Sacred Heart, these prayers surface in my heart...

_____
_____
_____
_____
_____

As I look to the day ahead, I offer these plans and tasks on my to-do list to you...

_____
_____
_____
_____
_____

My heart fills with gratitude and joy when I think of...

_____
_____
_____
_____
_____

Jesus, help me to surrender these concerns and crosses to you...

_____
_____
_____
_____
_____

I offer this all to you, my Jesus. Draw me ever closer
to your Sacred Heart today. Allow me to rest in you. Amen.

THE JOY OF
THE LORD

is your strength

NEHEMIAH 8:10

As I rise to begin the day, Jesus, these thoughts fill my mind...

_____
_____
_____
_____
_____

When I gaze into your Sacred Heart, these prayers surface in my heart...

_____
_____
_____
_____
_____

As I look to the day ahead, I offer these plans and tasks on my to-do list to you...

_____
_____
_____
_____
_____

My heart fills with gratitude and joy when I think of...

_____
_____
_____
_____
_____

Jesus, help me to surrender these concerns and crosses to you...

_____
_____
_____
_____
_____

I offer this all to you, my Jesus. Draw me ever closer
to your Sacred Heart today. Allow me to rest in you. Amen.

BE TO ME

a rock of

refuge

PSALM 71:3

_____ / _____ / _____

As I rise to begin the day, Jesus, these thoughts fill my mind...

_____
_____
_____
_____
_____

When I gaze into your Sacred Heart, these prayers surface in my heart...

_____
_____
_____
_____
_____

As I look to the day ahead, I offer these plans and tasks on my to-do list to you...

_____
_____
_____
_____
_____

My heart fills with gratitude and joy when I think of...

_____
_____
_____
_____
_____

Jesus, help me to surrender these concerns and crosses to you...

_____
_____
_____
_____
_____

I offer this all to you, my Jesus. Draw me ever closer
to your Sacred Heart today. Allow me to rest in you. Amen.

BLESS THE LORD

oh my soul

PSALM 103:1

As I rise to begin the day, Jesus, these thoughts fill my mind...

_____
_____
_____
_____
_____

When I gaze into your Sacred Heart, these prayers surface in my heart...

_____
_____
_____
_____
_____

As I look to the day ahead, I offer these plans and tasks on my to-do list to you...

_____
_____
_____
_____
_____

My heart fills with gratitude and joy when I think of...

_____
_____
_____
_____
_____

Jesus, help me to surrender these concerns and crosses to you...

_____
_____
_____
_____
_____

I offer this all to you, my Jesus. Draw me ever closer
to your Sacred Heart today. Allow me to rest in you. Amen.

RETURN TO ME

with all your heart

JOEL 2:12

As I rise to begin the day, Jesus, these thoughts fill my mind...

_____
_____
_____
_____
_____

When I gaze into your Sacred Heart, these prayers surface in my heart...

_____
_____
_____
_____
_____

As I look to the day ahead, I offer these plans and tasks on my to-do list to you...

_____
_____
_____
_____
_____

My heart fills with gratitude and joy when I think of...

_____
_____
_____
_____
_____

Jesus, help me to surrender these concerns and crosses to you...

_____
_____
_____
_____
_____

I offer this all to you, my Jesus. Draw me ever closer
to your Sacred Heart today. Allow me to rest in you. Amen.

THE LORD IS
MY LIGHT

*and my
salvation*

PSALM 27:1

As I rise to begin the day, Jesus, these thoughts fill my mind...

_____
_____
_____
_____
_____

When I gaze into your Sacred Heart, these prayers surface in my heart...

_____
_____
_____
_____
_____

As I look to the day ahead, I offer these plans and tasks on my to-do list to you...

_____
_____
_____
_____
_____

My heart fills with gratitude and joy when I think of...

_____
_____
_____
_____
_____

Jesus, help me to surrender these concerns and crosses to you...

_____
_____
_____
_____
_____

I offer this all to you, my Jesus. Draw me ever closer
to your Sacred Heart today. Allow me to rest in you. Amen.

TASTE AND SEE

that the Lord

is good

PSALM 34:8

_____/_____/_____

As I rise to begin the day, Jesus, these thoughts fill my mind...

_____
_____
_____
_____
_____

When I gaze into your Sacred Heart, these prayers surface in my heart...

_____
_____
_____
_____
_____

As I look to the day ahead, I offer these plans and tasks on my to-do list to you...

_____
_____
_____
_____
_____

My heart fills with gratitude and joy when I think of...

_____
_____
_____
_____
_____

Jesus, help me to surrender these concerns and crosses to you...

_____
_____
_____
_____
_____

I offer this all to you, my Jesus. Draw me ever closer
to your Sacred Heart today. Allow me to rest in you. Amen.

THE LORD
HAS DONE

great things

for us

PSALM 126:3

_____/_____/_____

As I rise to begin the day, Jesus, these thoughts fill my mind...

_____
_____
_____
_____
_____

When I gaze into your Sacred Heart, these prayers surface in my heart...

_____
_____
_____
_____
_____

As I look to the day ahead, I offer these plans and tasks on my to-do list to you...

_____
_____
_____
_____

My heart fills with gratitude and joy when I think of...

_____
_____
_____
_____

Jesus, help me to surrender these concerns and crosses to you...

_____
_____
_____
_____

I offer this all to you, my Jesus. Draw me ever closer
to your Sacred Heart today. Allow me to rest in you. Amen.

DO NOT FEAR

for I am

with you

ISAIAH 41:10

As I rise to begin the day, Jesus, these thoughts fill my mind...

_____

_____

_____

_____

_____

When I gaze into your Sacred Heart, these prayers surface in my heart...

_____

_____

_____

_____

_____

As I look to the day ahead, I offer these plans and tasks on my to-do list to you...

_____

_____

_____

_____

_____

My heart fills with gratitude and joy when I think of...

_____

_____

_____

_____

_____

Jesus, help me to surrender these concerns and crosses to you...

_____

_____

_____

_____

_____

I offer this all to you, my Jesus. Draw me ever closer
to your Sacred Heart today. Allow me to rest in you. Amen.

THERE IS
FORGIVENESS

with you

PSALM 130:4

_____/_____/_____

As I rise to begin the day, Jesus, these thoughts fill my mind...

_____
_____
_____
_____
_____

When I gaze into your Sacred Heart, these prayers surface in my heart...

_____
_____
_____
_____
_____

As I look to the day ahead, I offer these plans and tasks on my to-do list to you...

_____
_____
_____
_____
_____

My heart fills with gratitude and joy when I think of...

_____
_____
_____
_____
_____

Jesus, help me to surrender these concerns and crosses to you...

_____
_____
_____
_____
_____

I offer this all to you, my Jesus. Draw me ever closer
to your Sacred Heart today. Allow me to rest in you. Amen.

PUT A NEW
AND RIGHT SPIRIT

within me

PSALM 51:10

_____/_____/_____

As I rise to begin the day, Jesus, these thoughts fill my mind...

_____
_____
_____
_____
_____

When I gaze into your Sacred Heart, these prayers surface in my heart...

_____
_____
_____
_____
_____

As I look to the day ahead, I offer these plans and tasks on my to-do list to you...

_____
_____
_____
_____
_____

My heart fills with gratitude and joy when I think of...

_____
_____
_____
_____
_____

Jesus, help me to surrender these concerns and crosses to you...

_____
_____
_____
_____
_____

I offer this all to you, my Jesus. Draw me ever closer
to your Sacred Heart today. Allow me to rest in you. Amen.

WE ARE

His people

PSALM 100:3

As I rise to begin the day, Jesus, these thoughts fill my mind...

_____
_____
_____
_____
_____

When I gaze into your Sacred Heart, these prayers surface in my heart...

_____
_____
_____
_____
_____

As I look to the day ahead, I offer these plans and tasks on my to-do list to you...

_____
_____
_____
_____
_____

My heart fills with gratitude and joy when I think of...

_____
_____
_____
_____
_____

Jesus, help me to surrender these concerns and crosses to you...

_____
_____
_____
_____
_____

I offer this all to you, my Jesus. Draw me ever closer
to your Sacred Heart today. Allow me to rest in you. Amen.

HIS STEADFAST LOVE

endures

forever

PSALM 107:1

As I rise to begin the day, Jesus, these thoughts fill my mind...

_____
_____
_____
_____
_____

When I gaze into your Sacred Heart, these prayers surface in my heart...

_____
_____
_____
_____
_____

As I look to the day ahead, I offer these plans and tasks on my to-do list to you...

_____
_____
_____
_____
_____

My heart fills with gratitude and joy when I think of...

_____
_____
_____
_____
_____

Jesus, help me to surrender these concerns and crosses to you...

_____
_____
_____
_____
_____

I offer this all to you, my Jesus. Draw me ever closer
to your Sacred Heart today. Allow me to rest in you. Amen.

MAY HIS NAME

be forever

PSALM 72:17

_____/_____/_____

As I rise to begin the day, Jesus, these thoughts fill my mind...

_____
_____
_____
_____
_____

When I gaze into your Sacred Heart, these prayers surface in my heart...

_____
_____
_____
_____
_____

As I look to the day ahead, I offer these plans and tasks on my to-do list to you...

_____
_____
_____
_____
_____

My heart fills with gratitude and joy when I think of...

_____
_____
_____
_____
_____

Jesus, help me to surrender these concerns and crosses to you...

_____
_____
_____
_____
_____

I offer this all to you, my Jesus. Draw me ever closer
to your Sacred Heart today. Allow me to rest in you. Amen.

I HAVE
LOVED YOU

with an

everlasting love

JEREMIAH 31:3

_____/_____/_____

As I rise to begin the day, Jesus, these thoughts fill my mind...

_____
_____
_____
_____
_____

When I gaze into your Sacred Heart, these prayers surface in my heart...

_____
_____
_____
_____
_____

As I look to the day ahead, I offer these plans and tasks on my to-do list to you...

_____
_____
_____
_____
_____

My heart fills with gratitude and joy when I think of...

_____
_____
_____
_____
_____

Jesus, help me to surrender these concerns and crosses to you...

_____
_____
_____
_____
_____

I offer this all to you, my Jesus. Draw me ever closer
to your Sacred Heart today. Allow me to rest in you. Amen.

YOU HAVE COME

to fullness in Him

COLOSSIANS 2:10

_____/_____/_____

As I rise to begin the day, Jesus, these thoughts fill my mind...

_____
_____
_____
_____
_____

When I gaze into your Sacred Heart, these prayers surface in my heart...

_____
_____
_____
_____
_____

As I look to the day ahead, I offer these plans and tasks on my to-do list to you...

_____
_____
_____
_____
_____

My heart fills with gratitude and joy when I think of...

_____
_____
_____
_____
_____

Jesus, help me to surrender these concerns and crosses to you...

_____
_____
_____
_____
_____

I offer this all to you, my Jesus. Draw me ever closer
to your Sacred Heart today. Allow me to rest in you. Amen.

I CHOSE

you

JOHN 15:16

As I rise to begin the day, Jesus, these thoughts fill my mind...

_____
_____
_____
_____
_____

When I gaze into your Sacred Heart, these prayers surface in my heart...

_____
_____
_____
_____
_____

As I look to the day ahead, I offer these plans and tasks on my to-do list to you...

_____
_____
_____
_____
_____

My heart fills with gratitude and joy when I think of...

_____
_____
_____
_____
_____

Jesus, help me to surrender these concerns and crosses to you...

_____
_____
_____
_____
_____

I offer this all to you, my Jesus. Draw me ever closer
to your Sacred Heart today. Allow me to rest in you. Amen.

MY BELOVED IS MINE

and I am His

SONG OF SOLOMON 2:16

_____/_____/_____

As I rise to begin the day, Jesus, these thoughts fill my mind...

_____
_____
_____
_____
_____

When I gaze into your Sacred Heart, these prayers surface in my heart...

_____
_____
_____
_____
_____

As I look to the day ahead, I offer these plans and tasks on my to-do list to you...

_____
_____
_____
_____
_____

My heart fills with gratitude and joy when I think of...

_____
_____
_____
_____
_____

Jesus, help me to surrender these concerns and crosses to you...

_____
_____
_____
_____
_____

I offer this all to you, my Jesus. Draw me ever closer
to your Sacred Heart today. Allow me to rest in you. Amen.

TAKE DELIGHT

in the Lord

PSALM 37:4

As I rise to begin the day, Jesus, these thoughts fill my mind...

_____
_____
_____
_____
_____

When I gaze into your Sacred Heart, these prayers surface in my heart...

_____
_____
_____
_____
_____

As I look to the day ahead, I offer these plans and tasks on my to-do list to you...

_____
_____
_____
_____
_____

My heart fills with gratitude and joy when I think of...

_____
_____
_____
_____
_____

Jesus, help me to surrender these concerns and crosses to you...

_____
_____
_____
_____
_____

I offer this all to you, my Jesus. Draw me ever closer
to your Sacred Heart today. Allow me to rest in you. Amen.

LOOK TO HIM

and be radiant

PSALM 34:5

As I rise to begin the day, Jesus, these thoughts fill my mind...

_____
_____
_____
_____
_____

When I gaze into your Sacred Heart, these prayers surface in my heart...

_____
_____
_____
_____
_____

As I look to the day ahead, I offer these plans and tasks on my to-do list to you...

_____
_____
_____
_____
_____

My heart fills with gratitude and joy when I think of...

_____
_____
_____
_____
_____

Jesus, help me to surrender these concerns and crosses to you...

_____
_____
_____
_____
_____

I offer this all to you, my Jesus. Draw me ever closer
to your Sacred Heart today. Allow me to rest in you. Amen.

KNOW THAT
THE LORD

is God

PSALM 100:3

As I rise to begin the day, Jesus, these thoughts fill my mind...

_____
_____
_____
_____
_____

When I gaze into your Sacred Heart, these prayers surface in my heart...

_____
_____
_____
_____
_____

As I look to the day ahead, I offer these plans and tasks on my to-do list to you...

_____
_____
_____
_____
_____

My heart fills with gratitude and joy when I think of...

_____
_____
_____
_____
_____

Jesus, help me to surrender these concerns and crosses to you...

_____
_____
_____
_____
_____

I offer this all to you, my Jesus. Draw me ever closer
to your Sacred Heart today. Allow me to rest in you. Amen.

HE RESTORES

my soul

PSALM 23:3

_____/_____/_____

As I rise to begin the day, Jesus, these thoughts fill my mind...

_____
_____
_____
_____
_____

When I gaze into your Sacred Heart, these prayers surface in my heart...

_____
_____
_____
_____
_____

As I look to the day ahead, I offer these plans and tasks on my to-do list to you...

_____
_____
_____
_____
_____

My heart fills with gratitude and joy when I think of...

_____
_____
_____
_____
_____

Jesus, help me to surrender these concerns and crosses to you...

_____
_____
_____
_____
_____

I offer this all to you, my Jesus. Draw me ever closer
to your Sacred Heart today. Allow me to rest in you. Amen.

reflecting
on my morning
part two

We invite you again to take a few minutes to reflect on your current morning routine now that you've completed this journal. There are no right or wrong answers. Regardless of where you are at in your spiritual journey, this reflection simply provides the opportunity to come humbly before Him and invite Him into your days.

Three words that describe how I feel upon waking are...

_____
_____
_____
_____
_____

My morning routine currently consists of...

_____
_____
_____
_____
_____

Using this journal has helped me to connect with God by...

_____
_____
_____
_____
_____

Some other changes to my morning routine that have
helped me to begin the day more peacefully are...

_____

_____

_____

_____

_____

After my morning routine, I feel...

_____

_____

_____

_____

_____

Moving forward, I'd like to more fully invite God into my day by...

_____

_____

_____

_____

_____

additional guidance

Whether this is your first or your fiftieth journaling experience, we can all benefit from some additional guidance at times. Feel free to refer to this section whenever you feel stuck or need help unpacking your thoughts.

Spend a few minutes breathing in and breathing out these words from Scripture. Allow your body to experience a sense of calm with God before you proceed to the journaling page.

Inhale and pray these words.

JOY COMES

with the morning

PSALM 30:5

Exhale and pray these words.

As you begin to journal on the next page, try to write freely from the heart, pouring forth your prayers, works, joys, and sufferings to Him.

As I rise to begin the day, Jesus, these thoughts fill my mind...

Now is the time to take whatever is in your head and put it down on paper. What thoughts are currently swirling in your mind? Are you worried about something that happened in the past or concerned about a task that lies ahead? Are you excited or full of anticipation when you reflect on the day to come? Regardless of how you feel, no thought is too small or too trivial to share with Him. He knows all, sees all, and loves all.

When I gaze into your Sacred Heart, these prayers surface in my heart...

What intentions are near and dear to your heart? What would you like to ask of God today? What gifts or graces do you need? Is there a wound that needs healing? Is there an experience for which you need courage? What specifically in your life needs God's loving direction? Which friend needs God to make His loving presence known? What friend is struggling and needs His graces? Be specific and intentional, asking freely of our loving God. Do not hesitate to be courageous in naming the requests and intentions.

As I look to the day ahead, I offer these plans and tasks on my to-do list to you...

What meetings or appointments are on your schedule? Which friends or acquaintances do you plan to see? What small, seemingly mundane tasks will you need to accomplish today? As you mentally prepare yourself for the work that lies ahead, ask God to order your day in His peace. Surrender each aspect of your day to Him.

My heart fills with gratitude and joy when I think of...

Right now, in this moment, what are you grateful for? What blessings has God showered you with lately? How has He shown himself to be faithful? What requests has He answered? As you examine the small and large blessings of your life, use this section to praise Him for His abundant goodness.

Jesus, help me to surrender these concerns and crosses to you...

Who or what is causing you to despair? What struggles feel insurmountable or overwhelming? Whatever burdens you carry, take a moment to offer them to Him. He waits for you with open arms, grace and mercy flowing forth from His pierced side.

I offer this all to you, my Jesus. Draw me ever closer to your Sacred Heart today. Allow me to rest in you. Amen.

As you prepare to begin a new day, close your journaling time with either this short prayer or another one of your own choosing. Ask God to remain with you throughout the day and to sustain you with His grace.

my morning offering

Various saints and other holy women and men have set a wonderful example for us by beginning their day with God. Many of them even crafted their own unique morning prayers based on the beauty of their individual lives. We hear their wisdom in these words:

"I desire to sanctify every beat of my heart."
St. Therese of Lisieux

"All that we do without offering it to God is wasted."
St. John Vianney

"Every morning prepare your soul for a tranquil day."
St. Francis de Sales

In this space, we invite you to write your own morning offering prayer. Using your own words, express to God how and why you'd like to surrender your day to Him. Share with Him how you long to center yourself in His loving presence during the next 24 hours. Intentionally give him your prayers, works, joys, and sufferings.

Be as conversational as you would like. There are no right or wrong words when pouring out your heart to the One who loves you most and best of all.

notes

notes

connect

www.livetodaywellco.com
Instagram @livetodaywellco
facebook.com/livetodaywellco
#themorningofferingjournal
#livetodaywellco

est 2018

live today well

COLLECTIVE

Made in the USA
Las Vegas, NV
09 January 2021

15491536R00115